D1106829

WE LIVE IN THE COUNTRY

ROUNDABOUT AMERICA

Come, let us look at the ways of life
in our country. Let us go into out-of-the-way
corners, up on the hills and down in the
valleys, into city streets and village homes.
Let us see and get to know the people.
Here and there, roundabout America, are
friends worth knowing.

The *Roundabout America* stories
are vivid scenes from real life,
in short-story or longer form,
for younger readers.

WE LIVE
IN THE COUNTRY

Written and Illustrated by

Lois Lenski

J. B. Lippincott Company

Philadelphia, 1960

c. 3

Foreword

How do people live in the country?

*On farms—but all farms are not alike. The word
"farm" suggests cows and hogs, wheat and corn. But
many farms have none of these things. Some farms pro-
duce food, some clothing, while some provide shelter.*

*Let us visit a chicken farm in Connecticut, a cotton
farm in Arkansas, a sheep farm in Texas, and a tree farm
in Louisiana. Each of these farms is a world of its own.
On these farms, the children never milk a cow and never
ride on a load of hay.*

*What do they do? These stories will tell you. For the
kind of farm determines how the children live, work and
play—each in a different way.*

Let us make them our friends.

Lois Lenski

Contents

Verses

In the Country

The grass is green,
Tall trees are seen—
    In the country.

The sun shines bright
From morn till night—
    In the country.

The cars go past
Our house so fast—
    In the country.

Birds sing in the tree
As sweet as can be—
    In the country.

Get up with the sun,
Rest when day is done—
    In the country.

I may go far away,
But I'll come home to stay—
    In the country.

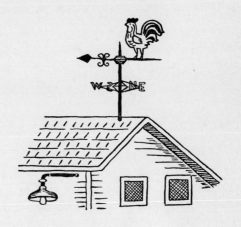

Kathy's Chickens

Kathy's Chickens

Breakfast Ready

Cock-a-doodle-dooo-o-o! A rooster crowed loudly.

"Oh, it's Saturday. I'm glad!"

Kathy Preston opened her eyes and looked out the window. It was still dark outside, but the lights were on in the hen house. They came on at five-thirty. So she knew it was morning. All the hens were cackling loudly.

Kathy dozed a while and woke again. She heard noises downstairs. She got up quietly. She

14

tried not to waken her little sister Susan.

Downstairs Roger, her brother, called out, "Get up, lazy bones! Breakfast is on the table."

Roger was eleven and felt much older than eight-year-old Kathy and five-year-old Susan.

Kathy dressed quickly. The bedroom was cold. The heat from the furnace did not get up to the second floor. Kathy put on her jeans to keep her legs warm. She looked out of the window. Most of the snow was gone. After the January thaw, it would snow hard again.

"It's Saturday! No school today!" Kathy was glad. Mama was frying pancakes. The smell came up the back stairs. "Goody! Pancakes! Maple syrup!"

Kathy went down the steps three at a time. Susan woke up and came down in her pajamas. Daddy had eaten and gone out. Mama put pancakes on the children's plates.

Kathy opened the back door and looked out. It was light now.

"Oh, Mama!" she cried. "Do you think they'll come today?"

Mama said, "It's time to eat your breakfast."

"But will they, Mama?" asked Kathy. "Will they come today?"

"What are you talking about?" said Mama. "I hope there's no company coming."

Susan laughed. "She means *the baby chicks!*"

"Oh, the chicks," said Mama. "I hope they will come today. I don't want them to stay in the post office over Sunday."

Kathy ran outside and looked at the thermometer.

"It's warmer," she said, coming in. "It's 34. They won't freeze if it's above 32, will they?"

"Don't worry about the chicks," said Mama. "If Mr. Bush keeps his car windows closed, they'll be all right."

Kathy clapped her hands. "I can hardly wait."

The day-old baby chicks were to be shipped by parcel post from a hatchery in a nearby Connecticut town.

Kathy ate her pancakes quickly. She was afraid the mailman would come.

Eggs

Roger went out to feed the hens, while Kathy and Susan washed the dishes. Kathy kept looking out the window. Two cars passed but not Mr. Bush's green one. Dishes done, Kathy sat down to help Mama with the eggs. Mama had to "candle" them all before she went to town.

Kathy wiped each egg clean with a cloth. Then Mama put each one on top of a round tin a foot high, which had a 150-watt electric bulb inside. If she saw any spots in the egg, she laid it aside. She weighed and sorted the eggs into sizes —small, large, jumbo and extra large. She packed them by the dozen into cardboard egg boxes. She put the egg boxes into an egg crate.

"Put the cracked eggs in that bowl there," said Mama. "I'll use them for supper."

The telephone rang two long and three short rings. "That's us," said Kathy. She ran to answer it.

"Hello!" said Kathy. "Yes . . . yes . . . one dozen . . . and two broilers. I'll tell her." She hung up the receiver.

"Mrs. White wants a dozen eggs today," said Kathy, "and two nice broilers for company."

"Bring me my list," said Mama, "so I can write it down. Two more broilers to be dressed."

Kathy looked out the window. "The mailman's late," she said. "I'd think he'd be on time when he's bringing baby chicks."

Mama looked at the clock. It was ten o'clock.

"Take the wire basket out to the hen house and bring in the eggs," she told Kathy. "Put on your coat—it's not summer yet."

A cold wind blew in when Kathy opened the door.

"But he might come . . ." she began.

"It's time to gather the eggs," said Mama.

Kathy crossed the barnyard to the laying

house. It was a long, two-story building made up of large rooms or pens, with fifty or more hens in each. Daddy had over two thousand chickens in all. Outside by the door was a large sign:

PRESTON CHICKEN FARM
Please
NO HORN

When people came in cars or trucks, Daddy did not want them to sound their horns, because it frightened the chickens.

Kathy went through the grain-room into the first chicken pen. Susan came behind her. A row of open nests was along one side. Hens were sitting on some of the nests to lay their eggs. Some were jumping off and cackling. Some were scratching in the straw on the floor. The room was very dusty. At the side, an open window let in fresh air. At the back were the perches where the hens roosted to sleep at night.

Kathy took eggs out of the nests. Some were cold to touch, but those freshly laid were warm. Kathy liked to hold them in her hand. She went into the next pen where there were more nests.

"Forty, forty-one . . ." she counted the eggs as she put them in the big wire basket. It was getting heavy, so Susan helped her carry it.

One hen would not get off the nest. She pecked at Kathy when she came near. "Let her alone!" said Kathy. "She's cross. She wants to set."

Roger came into the pen. He had two big buckets filled with feed. He was putting it in the hoppers for the hens to eat.

Just then an automobile horn sounded. It was blowing loud. The hens squawked and began to run.

"Who's that blowing his horn?" scolded Roger. "Who's trying to scare the hens?"

Kathy looked at Susan. They set the egg-basket down in the grain-room and ran. The mailman had come at last.

Baby Chicks

Out by the mailbox stood the mailman beside his car. He took five big flat boxes from the back seat. Mama was there with the wheelbarrow.

"Well, here they are, Mrs. Preston!" said Mr. Bush.

"On Saturday too!" said Kathy's mother. "When I have my hands full."

Cheep, cheep, cheep! Cheep, cheep, cheep! Kathy could hear all the little chicks peeping inside the boxes. The boxes had holes in them to give the chicks air.

Mr. Bush drove off and Mrs. Preston pushed the wheelbarrow to the brooder house. Daddy had started the coal stove inside, so the room was warm. Daddy opened the boxes and Kathy helped Mama lift the little chicks out. Susan watched. Then Mama went back to the house.

There were a hundred chicks in each box, five hundred in all. They were only a day old. They had been hatched the day before.

Kathy and Susan held some of them in their hands. They were light yellow, warm and fuzzy. They said "peep, peep, peep."

"They're hungry!" said Kathy. "Mr. Bush never fed them, I bet."

"They don't need feed the first day," said Daddy.

"Oh, I wish they had a Mama-hen to take care of them," said Kathy.

"Incubators hatch them better than Mama-hens, and more at one time," said Daddy.

Carefully he placed the little chicks under the big tin brooder hood.

"They'll be as warm and cozy here as if they were under the old Mama-hen," said Daddy.

"Can't I keep just one?" asked Kathy.

"No," said Daddy. "It's better off here. It would only die from the cold in the wintertime. Put it back."

Kathy held the baby chick close to her cheek and then put it with the others.

Soon all the chicks were in their new home.

They were quiet now. Daddy put some baby chick food in low feeders for them. Kathy filled the glass jars with warm water so they could drink. Then they went away and left them.

"I hope they like it on our chicken farm," said Kathy.

Kathy's Cats

Back in the kitchen, Mama was busy dressing chickens for people in town to buy. First she scalded them, picked the feathers off and singed them with a lighted newspaper. Then she cut them open and cleaned the insides out, but saved the heart, liver and gizzard. Kathy watched.

"Are we going to town soon?" she asked.

"As soon as I get my orders ready," said Mama.

She cut a chicken gizzard open and showed Kathy the stones inside.

"Just think! A chicken can eat stones!" said Kathy.

"It has no stomach," said Mama. "The stones digest the food."

Kathy saw a kitten on the window sill outside.

She opened the window and brought it in. She gave it a piece of chicken liver to eat.

"Oh, you mustn't give it the liver," said Mama. "And don't let the cats in when I'm dressing chickens."

"She's hungry," said Kathy. "She's got to eat."

Kathy had many cats, she did not know how many. Daddy called them "barn cats" but they lived in the hen house. There were at least three mothers and eight or ten little kittens. Daddy made a cat-hole for them to come in and out of the grain-room. They did not often come to the house.

Kathy put the kitten outside, but came back with a big cat in her arms. The cat jumped down to the pail of chicken waste and began to eat.

"What did I tell you?" said Mama.

Mama turned to Kathy as Kathy reached for the cat. Mama scolded.

"I told you to keep those cats out of here. Take them to the hen house to catch rats."

Kathy said, "They don't like rats. Chicken tastes better."

Peddling Eggs

After dinner, Mama got ready to go to town. Her eggs and the dressed chickens were all in the car. Kathy and Susan went with her. They wore their heavy coats, and had scarves over their heads.

At first it was fun. They stopped at people's houses on the way. Mrs. Dave Green was not at home, so Mama left her eggs next door. Mrs. White lived up a steep hill. She came to the door for her eggs and the broilers. She told about her company coming. Mrs. Moore had no change and had to go to her neighbor to get it. Her children talked to Kathy and Susan.

Then they were in town. Mama took her list out of her purse and read the names on it. She drove up one street and down another. She stopped so many times Kathy lost count. At Mrs. Martin's house, her children were playing in the street. They came up to talk.

"My, you're late today," said Mrs. Martin. "Cold, isn't it? Do you have change?" She gave back two empty boxes.

Mrs. Martin's neighbor came out. "Got an

extra dozen?" she asked. "It sure is nice to get
fresh eggs from the country."

Mama went on. She stopped at big houses and
little houses, and sometimes at a store. She went
in back doors and side doors. Once she stayed so
long, Susan began to cry. The girls were getting
tired now. It was not fun any more.

"Why did you stay so long, Mama?" asked
Kathy.

"Old Mrs. Craig was sick and I tried to cheer
her up," said Mama.

"I thought you were never coming," said Susan. "I want to go home."

Mama went into Tom's Laundry next. There were pretty house plants in the window and a little Chinese girl stood in the doorway. She smiled at Kathy and said hello. She said her name was Diane Wong. Diane said she had no one to play with.

"Would you like to have a kitty, Diane?" asked Kathy.

"Oh yes," said the little girl.

"I'll bring you one next Saturday," said Kathy, "when we bring the eggs."

Diane said, "Thank you. Don't forget." She waved good-by.

"Only one more stop," said Mama on the way home.

It was at Holt's Country Store. Mr. Holt took a crateful of eggs from the trunk of Mama's car. There were thirty dozen in the crate. Mama traded the eggs for groceries. She got enough for the whole family to eat all week.

And she got a candy bar for Kathy and one for Susan.

On the Range

Cackle, cackle, cackle! Cackle, cackle, cackle!
Squawk, squawk, squawk!

Something was wrong in the brooder house. Kathy and Susan ran and looked in. It was not a rat or a stray dog scaring the chickens. Daddy and Roger were catching them. Feathers and dust were flying. They put the chickens in crates in the back of Daddy's truck.

Kathy and Susan climbed up in the cab. Roger put the last crate in and jumped on behind. Daddy drove down the back lane to the range.

It was April now, a bright sunny day. The baby chicks that had come in January were now twelve weeks old, about half grown. They had to be moved out of the brooder house, to make way for a new shipment of five hundred baby chicks.

The range was a big field planted to clover, where the chickens could run loose. In it were a dozen or more range shelters. These shelters were low coops that held a hundred and twenty-five chickens each. They had floors made of perches, so the droppings fell on the ground beneath. Daddy began to unload.

"You girls get out of the way!" shouted Roger.

"I want to help," said Kathy.

"There's nothing you can do," said Daddy. "Stay in the cab."

The girls watched. Daddy and Roger opened the crates and put the chickens into four of the shelters.

"We'll keep them penned up for a few days till they get used to it here," said Daddy. "They are always strange at first, and act scary."

A few days later, Roger and Kathy went to the range to give the chickens water. Now they were

let out on the range. They found their way to the
end of the lot and back to their own coops again.
Water was piped to the range, but Roger had to
draw it and carry it in pails. Kathy helped.

Suddenly a large bird flew over the range. It
circled around as if looking for something. Its
shadow fell on the ground. The chickens began
to squawk and run. They all piled into the nearest
shelter, pell-mell. They crowded on top of each
other.

"O-o-oh! What was it?" wailed Kathy. "An
eagle? It was bigger than a crow."

"That was a chicken hawk," said Roger. "If we hadn't been here, it would have swooped down and caught a chicken. They seem to know it. They always run for cover."

Roger went into the shelter. He shooed the chickens out again.

"They were piled up in a tight pile," he said. "If they had stayed that way, those underneath would have died."

Suddenly the loud roar of a motor was heard overhead. An airplane flying low went over. The chickens squawked and ran again.

"Why are they scared now?" asked Kathy. "An airplane won't hurt them."

"It looks like a chicken hawk to them," said Roger. "That was Mr. Alcorn spraying his potato field. If he keeps on scaring our hens, they'll all stop laying. Fright causes blood spots in the eggs too."

Kathy and Roger walked back up the lane.

"They're scared of dogs and cats and birds and rats and automobile horns and strange people and loud noises..." said Kathy. "I wonder why."

"That's chicken nature," said Roger.

The White Rooster

"Hold this door open," said Roger to Kathy. "I've got to feed laying mash to the hens, but first I'll take old Jumbo out. *He's* not going to lay!"

Roger went to the last pen, where a large white rooster stayed. The children hated this rooster and called him Jumbo.

"Better take the croquet mallet with you," said Kathy.

"I'm not afraid of Jumbo!" bragged Roger. "It'd take a lot more than a dumb old rooster to scare me."

Daddy was catching hens. Kathy left the pen door open and went inside to watch Daddy. A large pen hung on the wall. It had bars in front. He was putting hens inside it.

"These hens are broody, they want to set," said Daddy. "I'll pen them up and they'll get over it."

"Can't I set a hen and hatch out some eggs?" asked Kathy.

"Better ask Mama about that," said Daddy.

Kathy's cats crowded round, meowing.

"Those cats act starved," said Daddy. "Why don't they catch rats?"

"I'll feed them," said Kathy. She gave them milk and dog-food. "They're not dogs, but they like dog-food," she said.

Suddenly she heard someone shouting. Could it be Roger? There he was, running. Jumbo, the old white rooster, was after him. Daddy came and looked too. Kathy and Daddy laughed. Roger, who was never scared of anything, was running fast, chased by the big old rooster.

Roger went flying over a stone wall with barbed wire on top. Daddy gave chase and caught Jumbo by the leg. Roger came back

ashamed. No one teased him, for he had a bad
gash in his leg from the rooster's beak and many
cuts from the barbed wire. Mama had to band-
age him up.

"Roosters can be plenty vicious!" said Daddy.

"Jumbo's days are numbered," said Mama.
"It's time he ended up in a pot. But oh, how
tough he will be!"

The Mother Hen

Kathy named her hen Henrietta. She put thir-
teen of Mama's best hatching eggs under her.
The hen's box sat in the entry of the grain-room.
There Kathy fed her daily and gave her water,
although the hen was very cross.

Twenty-one days was a long time to wait. Kathy and Susan grew very anxious. They looked at the eggs every time Henrietta got off the nest, but saw no change in them.

At last Susan saw a crack in an egg. Kathy saw one too. Then things began to happen fast. Soon all the eggs were cracking. The next day there were ten baby chicks in the nest. They were weak and damp. They could not walk. Kathy and Susan were so excited, they ran and told Mama all about it.

The next morning, the baby chicks were all hidden under the mother hen. One stuck its head out from the mother's wing. Then Henrietta stood up, and the girls could see them. The chicks were soft and fluffy. They said "peep, peep, peep."

Mama chopped hard-boiled eggs and Kathy gave it to the chicks, but they did not know how to eat. The mother hen had to show them how. She clucked. She picked up food in her beak. She dropped it, so the chicks would pick it up. The next day they were ready for chick feed. Soon they could eat and drink water too. Kathy and

Susan took care of them.

Henrietta and her baby chicks lived in the yard by the house. They grew tame and came to the back door. They were not scary like the young chicks in the brooder house that had no mother hen. They were not scared of dogs or cats or people. Sometimes they came in the kitchen and ate crumbs off the floor. Mama did not like it and shooed them out. She told the girls to take them to the chicken yard.

Kathy and Susan watched the chickens grow. Soon they lost their fluffy look and grew little stiff feathers. Their necks and legs grew longer.

After a time, Henrietta went away and left them to take care of themselves. So Daddy put them on the range with the others, and Henrietta went back to the laying house.

One day Kathy and Susan were gathering eggs.

"That's Henrietta there!" said Kathy pointing. "She's laying eggs again."

"Yes," said Susan, "for another family of baby chicks!"

Home from School

Winter had come again. It was very cold one morning, so Mama had the coal stove going. In warm weather, she used the electric stove, but she liked the coal stove to help heat the house in winter. She mixed up a batch of bread and put a pot of pork and beans in the oven.

The school bus was late because of the snow. On the way home it got stuck in the ditch several times. Roger and Kathy thought they would never get home. When they did, Mama and Daddy were not there.

"I bet they went over to Aunt Dorothy's," said

Kathy. "Mama wanted to borrow a pattern from her."

"I'm going coasting," said Roger. "It's slick down on the hill in the back lot. Bobby Alcorn's waiting for me."

"Feed the chickens first," said Kathy, "and I'll gather the eggs. And don't forget—Mama said for you to take the ashes out."

Roger was in a hurry to go, but first he had his chores to do. He fed the chickens and took the ashes out.

Kathy was lonely after he left. Susan was with

Mama, and she missed her. The house was so quiet, she could hear the clock ticking. The telephone kept ringing, but it was always someone else's ring, not the Prestons'. Kathy brought three of the kittens in and played with them on the couch. She gave them names, Sandy, Candy and Dandy. She played the kittens went to school and she was the teacher.

Then Mama and Daddy and Susan came back from Aunt Dorothy's, and soon the pork and beans were on the table. Roger came in, his cheeks red from the cold.

"Gee! That wind's enough to cut a person in two! But coasting was wonderful!"

He threw off his wraps and they all sat down to eat supper.

Emergency

About seven o'clock, a loud knock came at the door, and a man put his head in. It was Mr. Alcorn, the neighbor down the road.

"Your hen house is on fire!" he cried excitedly.

"On FIRE!" Daddy jumped up.

"Didn't you know?" said Mr. Alcorn. "We

saw the flames clear up at our place."

"Ring the operator," called Daddy. "Give a general alarm and ask for help!"

The hen house was to the north and the kitchen to the south, so no one had seen the flames. The children ran out in the snow and looked.

Mama called the telephone operator. That would bring help quickly. There were fifteen families on the party line.

The men rushed to get water. Chickens aflame were flying out where the roof had burned away.

The smell of burning feathers and the frightened cackling of the chickens filled the air. The wind blew the flames toward the house.

"What will we do if it takes our house?"

The children crowded round Mama and held her tight.

Neighbors came quickly with milk pails in their hands. They filled them at the pump and threw water on the flames. Some brought large cream cans full of water. They threw it on the side of the house to keep the fire from catching.

"It's so close to the house," Mama said. "Why did we build the hen house so close to the house?"

Men and women crowded around trying to help.

Then Mrs. Alcorn said, "The wind has changed."

It was true. Gradually the flames died down. Some of the people went home, others stayed to watch, in case the wind started the fire again.

At last, Daddy told Mama and the children to go inside.

"Where's Kathy?" asked Mama.

"She was just here," said Roger.

"No, she was scared, she went in the house,"
said Susan.

Mama hurried to the back door. There she saw
a strange sight. Bedding and clothing were lying
out in the snow. Two chairs were there, with
kitchen pans on them. Quilts and towels had been
thrown from an open upstairs window.

"I saved them!" cried Kathy at the window, excited and proud. She looked down at Mama.
"I didn't want our clothes and chairs to get
burned up!"

"Goodness sakes!" said Mama in a low voice. "They might have burned outside here too."

But no one scolded Kathy. Daddy called her "his brave girl" and said how proud he was.

They all gathered up the blankets and pillows and shoes and towels out of the snowbank by the house.

"Good thing I have the coal stove going," said Mama.

They spread the things around the warm kitchen to dry them.

Some of the men stayed to see that there was no more danger. Mama and Mrs. Alcorn made coffee and gave them sandwiches. They sat in the living room talking. They wondered how the fire had started.

That night the Prestons went to bed with thankful hearts that it had been no worse. But when morning came, they felt very blue.

"Oh, those poor chickens!" said Mama. "I wish we'd never gone in the chicken business. All our layers are gone . . . No eggs to sell all winter . . . My poor customers in town . . ."

"Be thankful we still have a home," said

Daddy. "The one thing I can't figure out is how it ever started. Now if it had been the brooder house I could understand it, but I won't start the brooder stove till the baby chicks come in January."

The source of the fire was a mystery.

About two o'clock the next day, a procession of trucks came up the road. They turned in at the Prestons' lane.

"Is that the feed-store truck?" called Daddy. "I phoned him not to come. I have no hens to feed."

Mama went out to see who it was. Daddy came too. The trucks were piled high with chicken crates, each filled with chickens of every breed and color.

Mr. Alcorn spoke up. "We thought we'd give you folks a little donation party!"

Daddy looked at Mama and smiled. Tears came to Mama's eyes. "Our good neighbors!" she said. "What would we do without them?"

The men stepped down and began unloading the chickens. They put them in the brooder house. They were all laying hens. Jim Alcorn

and Tom Hornby had gone out that morning and stopped at every farm for miles around. They got chickens from each farmer.

Daddy counted as they unloaded. There were many more hens than had burned.

"Guess I'll have to order a truckload of feed after all," said Daddy. "Roger, go phone the feed store."

"And I'll be able to take eggs to my customers in town," said Mama.

"When you rebuild that chicken house," said

Jim Alcorn, "put it a little farther away from your house, won't you?"

"We will," said Mama and Daddy. "How can we ever thank you?"

Roger was very quiet for many weeks after the fire. Kathy said to him every day, "Why don't you tell? You'll feel better if you do."

At last Roger told. He had been in such a hurry to empty the coal ashes the day of the fire, he had dumped them beside the hen house without thinking.

Roger had punished himself. So Daddy was glad to hear him say, "I'll try to *think* after this."

Daddy patted him on the back.

"Was it roast chicken you wanted, son?"

Roger looked up and laughed.

Mama and Kathy and Susan laughed too.

Here Comes the Mailman

Here comes the mailman—what will he bring?
A letter, a package, most anything.

Sometimes he's early, sometimes he's late,
I like to be waiting out by the gate.

I hear a horn blowing—can that be he?
Out very fast I go running to see.

Here comes the mailman, bringing the mail,
Run! Let's go meet him without fail.

A Dress for Jinny

A Dress for Jinny

At Home

"You'll have to fix dinner, sugar," said Mama.

"Tell me what to do," said the little girl.

"First, light the oil burner and put the skillet on," said Mama. "Then git some 'taters out of the sack. Peel 'em and cut 'em up, then when the grease is hot, put 'em in."

Jinny Harris was eight, a thin little girl with short, blond hair. She went to the kitchen and set to work.

Mama was sick in bed. She had been in the hospital for over a week, but now she was back home. Daddy would not let her come to the cotton field. He said she was too sick to chop cotton.

"Daddy and Don will soon be in," said Mama. "They didn't take their lunch. Git that head of cabbage out and cut it up for cole slaw."

Four-year-old Susie ran in. "Mama, I'm hungry," she said. Behind her came little Bobby, age two. "Me hungry too," he said. They climbed up on Mama's bed.

"Jinny's fixin' dinner," Mama said. "Purty soon you can eat."

They bounced on the bed until Mama told them to get off.

"Susie, go set the table for Jinny," said Mama.

Susie climbed on a chair and took cups out of the cupboard. She set them on the cook-table. Then she and Bobby began to chase each other. They knocked a chair over, and a broom fell down.

"Oh, Mama," said Jinny, "I'm afraid they'll knock the cook-table over. And they keep gittin' in my way all the time."

"Susie and Bobby, you go outside and play,"

said Mama.

Jinny shooed them out the back door.

"Every house we git is so little," Jinny said, "we can't hardly turn around in it. There's not much room to have any fun in this house, Mama. How long we gonna live here?"

"Just a year, I reckon," said Mama.

"Then we got to move again?" asked the girl.

"I reckon so," said Mama.

Jinny had moved so many times, once each year in all her eight years. Daddy was a share-cropper, so he had no home of his own. He shared the crop of a cotton farmer. He had no tractor, no horses or mules, not even hoes to chop cotton. All he had was a wife and four children, a few pieces of furniture and an old used car.

The boss-man Daddy worked for gave them a house to live in, a truck to drive, tools and a tractor to use. In return, Daddy planted and picked ten acres of cotton, and gave the boss-man half of what he got for it.

All the family had to work to get the crop out. Now, in early summer, Daddy and Don, who was eleven, were chopping the cotton. They had to chop all the weeds out of the row and thin the cotton plants where they were planted too thick. Jinny could not help. She had to stay at home and take care of Mama and the little ones.

Jinny remembered when they moved to this house six months before. It was cold winter, in January. The family came in the car and the furniture came in the boss-man's truck. When they unloaded, one leg of the cook-table got broken, so Daddy propped it up with a brick. The other furniture was old and shaky, but it still held together.

There was one thing new, though—linoleum for the floor—with a border around it like a rug! At the last house where they lived, there was enough money left over to buy it! The rug had red roses on it. Jinny scolded the little ones when they tracked mud on the rug. She mopped it every day.

"Why do we have to move so many times?" asked Jinny.

Mama sounded sad. "If the crop is good, the boss-man and Daddy both make money," she said. "If it's poor, there's less for the boss-man and less for us. If there's no crop, there's nothin' for nobody."

"Can't we ever stay two years in one house?" asked the girl.

"Sharecroppers mostly keep movin' on," said Mama. "Maybe the next boss-man and the next crop will be better."

"At our next house do you think there'll be a tree?" asked Jinny. She looked out the window at the sea of green. Cotton was growing right up close to the house, as far away as she could see.

"Maybe," said Mama. "You can't ever tell."

"The hot sun makes me feel sick sometimes," said Jinny. "Just one tree would make a little shade." She stopped and dreamed a little. "This year, do you think we'll git a new cook-table— without a broken leg?"

"I don't know," said Mama. "We got to be as savin' as we can. You're not always happy by gittin' things."

Mama had been sick ever since the Harrises came to this house. That was why Jinny did not like it much. Every day she made up the beds, swept the floor and mopped it as well as she could. But the house never looked right to her. It never seemed like home.

Soon Don and Daddy came in. They helped put the dinner on the table. Jinny took a plate in to Mama, but she did not eat much. Little Bobby found a can of evaporated milk, turned it up and drained it dry. There was never any fresh milk to drink.

Daddy tipped his chair back against the wall to rest a while.

"Cotton's growin' mighty fast," he said. "Choppin' will soon be over. Then we'll lay the

crop by, and after that we'll pick."

"Will it be a big crop this year, Daddy?" asked Jinny.

"Oh, so-so!" said Daddy. "If we git just enough rain and not too much, and just enough sun and not too much . . . we'll make out, I reckon. You kids can do a big job a-pickin' this year. You're a year older than you were at Johnson's place."

Jinny knew all about cotton. Cotton was her life. The seed was planted in the spring and the plants grew fast all summer. The pretty pink and white blossoms dropped off and left hard green bolls. In the fall, the bolls began to burst, and there were the fluffs of white cotton, all ready to be picked.

"What we got to pick *for?*" asked Jinny.

"Daddy just told you," said Don. "To git the crop out. So he can sell it at the gin and git money for it."

"Money to buy food and clothes with," added Daddy.

"And other things we need," said Mama.

Jinny knew all about a cotton gin. She often

went there with Daddy and watched. A big pipe
sucked up the cotton right out of the truck. Inside the gin, a machine picked the seeds out of the
cotton and threw them out in a heap on the
ground. Another machine pressed the cotton into
bales. The bales were loaded high on a big truck
and Uncle Joe hauled them away.

"Where do the big bales go?" asked Jinny.

"Uncle Joe hauls them to the city," said
Daddy. "They go to factories all over the country, and all over the world."

"What *for?*" asked Jinny.

"Now that's a hard one." Daddy laughed.
"The factories make things. I heard a man on the
radio tellin' what-all they make out of cotton—
hats and socks and curtains and writing paper
and fertilizer and soap and stock feed and gun-
powder . . ."

The children laughed.

Mama spoke from the next room. "You forgot
the most important thing—yard goods. The cotton bales go to the weaving mills to make cloth.
They make cotton cloth for shirts and pants and
for sheets and towels. They make pretty cloth for

dresses."

"They do?" asked Jinny. She looked down at the dress she wore. "Is my dress cotton?"

"It sure is," said Mama. "Once we visited Aunt Lucy and saw the weaving mill where she works. Guess you were too little to remember. They make yard goods there."

"Every little ole dress you ever had came straight from the cotton field!" said Daddy, getting up to go. "Whenever I look at a big field of cotton, I can see two clean sheets for every person in the world!"

"And if I pick enough cotton," said Jinny, "will they make it into a new dress for me?"

Daddy patted her on the head.

"They sure will, sugar!" he said. "And we'll make a special trip to town to buy it."

In the Field

"Is night a-comin' soon?" asked Jinny.

The cotton field was large and the cotton was as tall as she was. The girl looked very small, with her long white pick-sack trailing behind her.

"Not till the sun goes down," said Don. "Look

how high it is. Are you tired already?"

"No, not very," said Jinny.

The green cotton plants were dotted all over now with puffs of white cotton. Jinny moved slowly down her row, picking them and putting them into her sack.

"What you thinkin' about, Jinny?" asked Don, looking back.

"I'm thinkin' about lots of things," said the girl. "I'm thinkin' about what I'll git when the crop's all picked."

"Candy? Ice cream? Gum? Peanuts?"

"None of them things," said Jinny. "You eat 'em up and they're gone. I'll git me somethin' to *keep*."

"What?" asked Don.

"I'll git me a new dress," said Jinny. "A real purty dress. One with ruffles on it."

"Better pick faster then," said Don. "Fancy dresses cost a lot."

The children picked a while, then the boy said, "What's that I hear? Music?"

"It's the radio in the car," said Jinny. "Listen how purty it is. Susie's got the window open so we can hear."

Smiles broke out on both their faces.

"Is that Bobby singin'?" asked Jinny.

"Cryin', more likely," said Don. "I bet Susie hit him. You better go and see. Here, take the key."

Don dug the car key out of his pocket. The two little children had been locked in the car for safe-keeping.

Jinny took her sack off her shoulder, and went over to the car. Bobby and Susie were sitting in front on the ragged and torn seat. The radio was going full-blast, as Susie turned the knobs. Little Bobby was behind the steering wheel, crying.

Jinny unlocked the door and opened it. She turned the radio down.

"You-all want something to eat?" she asked.

Susie nodded, so Jinny took crackers out of a box and fed them.

"You-all want a drink of water?" she asked.

Again Susie nodded. A two-quart jar of water was on the floor in the back. Jinny held the jar up and both children drank. Jinny climbed in the back seat to rest. It was good to get out of the sun for a while.

Then Susie slipped out of the car with her little

tow sack. She ran over to where Don was pick-ing and said, "I gotta pick cotton."

"You come right back here," called Jinny. "Mama told you to stay in the car with Bobby to-day."

Jinny ran after Susie but could not catch her. Then she saw that Bobby had climbed out of the car too, toy truck in hand. He sat down to play in the dirt.

"You'd better lock the kids up in the car again," called Don, "or Mama'll whup the but-tons off your dress!"

Jinny chased Susie but could not catch her. So she came back to her row and began to pick cot-ton again.

"I have to keep on pickin'," she said. "I wanna help Daddy git his crop out."

Jinny's hands moved back and forth quickly, tucking the white puffs of cotton into her sack. She looked up now and then and called, "Susie, you come back here. Here's your sack. Come help me pick."

At last Susie came. Jinny hung the four-foot tow sack around her neck. "Now you pick," she said.

Susie set to work. She counted her bolls as she picked. "One, two, four, six, nine, three, fourteen . . ."

Jinny counted for her, making a little rhyme:

"I pick one, I've just begun,
I pick two, I've lost my shoe.
I pick three, where can Susie be?
I pick four, don't bang the car door!"

But Susie was not listening. Don had gone far ahead now on his row. Don was a good picker and seldom stopped. He tried to get 170 pounds every day.

"Look there!" Don shouted back. "You left the car door open. Bobby has climbed out too."

"Oh, he's all right," said Jinny. "He's playin' there in the dirt with his little truck."

"Keep your eye on him," said Don.

Jinny had to keep her eye on Susie, on Bobby, and on her own row of cotton. No wonder she could not pick as fast as Don.

"I wanna weigh up now," said Susie, stopping work.

"Why, you haven't even got five pounds," said Jinny. "You keep on picking."

Jinny looked over toward the car, but did not see Bobby's little yellow head above the cotton row.

"He's layin' down playin'," she said to herself.

She kept on picking and she coaxed Susie to pick. Then she looked again. Still she did not see Bobby. Worried, she took off her sack and ran over to the car.

Bobby was not there. His little truck was lying in the dirt. The children's lunch sack was in the dirt too. Boloney and crackers and cheese were spilled.

Jinny looked in front and back of the car and underneath. But no little boy was there. She

looked up and down the turn-row but did not see
him. Then she got scared. *Where had Bobby
gone?*

"*Don! Oh, Don!*" she called. There was panic
in her voice. "Bobby's gone! I can't find him!"

Don heard and this time he stopped work and
came over.

"Daddy'll whup you for leavin' the car door
open," he said.

In tears Jinny could not speak. She took Susie
by the hand and the three children started to
hunt. Up and down the cotton rows they went,
but no Bobby. Where could he have gone so
quickly?

Over on the far side of the field, a quarter of a mile away, Daddy and Uncle Joe were picking. Don ran over and told them. They stopped picking to look. Daddy started the car and drove up and down the turn-rows, honking his horn.

People picking in the next field came over to see what was wrong. Men and women spread out through the rows, hunting for the lost boy.

Daddy sent Jinny and Susie home. Little Susie cried all the way. At home, Mama cried too when Jinny told her the news. Mama tried to get out of bed to go and hunt, but she felt too sick.

It seemed a long time before Daddy came back with a sleepy, tired little boy on his arm.

"He went to the wrong end of the field," said Daddy, "clear down by the by-o. Then he musta got tired and fell asleep on the bank. When I got there, I thought I saw the weeds a-movin'. I called his name and there he come a-stumblin' out of the soybean patch. The sweat was a-pourin' off him like rain, and when he saw me he begun to cry ... Then his daddy picked him up and toted him home."

Mama took her baby in her arms. "If he'd a-walked the other way, he'd a-gone straight into the water. But he come right to his daddy's arms—and now we got him safe." She smiled through her tears.

Jinny never got whipped at all. Mama was so glad the little boy was found, she did not even scold her for letting the little ones out of the car. Jinny was happy again.

In Town

"How much did I git?" asked Jinny.

"Thirty-nine pounds this time," said Daddy.

"Whew! You're doin' fine, sugar."

Daddy marked it down in his little green book. Then he lifted her sack off the scales at the back of the trailer.

"That makes 120 pounds for you today," he said. "Workin' hard to git that new dress, ain't you?"

Jinny nodded.

"Soon you'll beat your big brother," said Daddy. "Don only made 150 today."

"I'd a-got still more," said Jinny, "but all them

stingin' worms was on the leaves. Two worms got on my sack and one was crawlin' up my stomach and one was on my leg a-stingin' me."

Daddy laughed. The girl climbed up on the trailer-load and emptied the cotton out of her sack. Susie and Bobby were up there bouncing.

When the trailer was full, it held a bale of cotton. But picking was slow now, and they could not fill it in a day, even with Mama helping. Mama was better and out in the field again.

When Daddy had only part of a load, he did not take it to the gin. He stored the cotton on the front porch to keep it out of the rain. So the porch was overflowing. Some of the cotton was in tow sacks, and some was loose in a large pile. That day they all went home early and the children ran to the front porch to play.

"Come here, Bobby!" called Jinny. "Come, let's go sleep-y!"

The children climbed up on the pile of cotton and fell tumbling down. They moved the tow sacks around and sat on them. They put them in a row to make a big bed. Jinny and Susie lay down and pretended to go to sleep.

Little Bobby climbed up between them. He got right in the middle, fell between two sacks and hit the floor with a thump. It hurt him but he laughed. Jinny kissed the bump.

Up drove Daddy in the boss-man's truck.

"Git off the cotton," he said. "I'm taking it all to the gin. This is the very last load! Cotton pickin's over for another year!"

The children watched as Daddy and Don loaded the cotton into the truck. They waved as Daddy drove off.

The very next Saturday, the Harris family went to town in their car. Daddy had been paid off and Mama wanted to buy winter clothes and groceries.

It was fun to go to town. Jinny did not go often. All the time Mama was sick, she had to stay at home with her and the little ones. It was November now and the air was cold. Jinny and Don and Susie sat in the back seat. They wore their old sweaters and coats from last year.

"We can't miss no Western on Saturday," said Daddy.

So the first place they went was to the show, and

after that, to the big general store. Jinny helped
Mama remember all the things they had to get.
Groceries first—flour and white soup beans,
canned milk, baking powder, soap and potatoes.

Then whom should they meet but Uncle Joe
and his family! So they all had to stop and visit
and tell the latest news. After Uncle Joe went
away, Mama and Daddy went to the furniture
department and picked out a new cook-table.
Then Daddy and Don bought new overalls and
shirts and shoes, because all their old ones were
worn out.

"Mama . . ." Jinny began, "are you gonna git
me . . . a new dress?"

"Our money's near-about gone," said Mama.
"I must watch every penny. The winter's gonna
be cold and long-lastin'."

"My old dress is a sight," said Jinny. "It's tore
in two places."

"I mended it," said Mama. "It don't look too
bad now."

"My jeans is all raggedy," Jinny went on.
"Every pair of 'em is in holes. My knees are all
the time a-peekin' through."

"I know it," said Mama. "I been seein' it. They're in rags."

"I git tired a-wearin' pants all the time, Mama," said Jinny. "I'd like to wear a dress . . . a purty dress."

Mama went to the jeans counter, looked over the big stack of jeans and held a pair up in front of the girl.

"We'll git 'em big," said Mama. "You're growin' so fast."

Next they went to the sweater counter and

Mama picked out a pretty red one. But Jinny did not look at it. New jeans and sweater could not take the place of a new dress.

"Daddy said if I picked cotton," Jinny began again, "they'd make it in a new dress for me . . ."

But Mama did not listen. She had many things on her mind. She had to buy overalls and underclothes and socks and shoes for the little ones. Jinny began to think Mama had forgotten all about her new dress. She felt very sad and the tears began to come.

Then Daddy came back. Daddy was feeling good and he said, "Got that girl o' mine a new dress yet?"

Mama laughed and said, "No, not yet."

"Well, go and git it," said Daddy. "She picked cotton enough to make ten dresses, but don't buy her but one!"

Jinny's heart lifted. They went to the corner where all the racks were hung with little girls' dresses. Jinny held on tight to Susie and Bobby, while Mama looked the dresses over. They were all so pretty—pink, blue, yellow, all the colors of the rainbow, and they all had fluffy full skirts that stood out like balloons. Which one would Mama choose? Jinny closed her eyes to keep from looking. She wanted it to be a surprise.

But Mama did not choose at all. She was turning away. She was not buying any of them. What was the matter? Wasn't she going to get a new dress after all?

Mama was walking to another part of the store. Jinny had to hurry to keep up, pulling Susie and Bobby behind her.

"But Mama . . ." wailed Jinny. "You didn't . . . They're so purty!"

"Purty, yes," said Mama, "but they cost a fortune. We haven't that much money. Besides, they're made out of nylon or some such stuff. I won't throw good money away on it. I want a dress I can wash and iron and mend and patch, a dress that wears like iron."

"But Daddy said . . ." began Jinny.

"He said you picked enough cotton for ten dresses," said Mama, "so I'll git you one—a cotton dress. I'll buy yard goods to sew. I have a sewing machine and I'll make it myself."

"Will it have ruffles on it?" asked Jinny.

"Yes," said Mama, "and pockets too."

Jinny felt better. The clerk showed them roll after roll of cotton cloth in pretty colors. It was hard to choose from so many. At last Jinny found a pretty pink piece with blue flowers all over it. It was prettier than any of the dresses on the rack. Mama paid for it, Jinny took the package and they left the store.

On the way home, Daddy asked about it. Jinny opened the package and showed him the cotton cloth.

"Whew!" whistled Daddy. "That's purty enough for a queen!"

"And it's cotton, Daddy," said Jinny happily, "because I picked all that cotton for you!"

"You're a lucky girl, sugar!" said Daddy.

Saturday Night

When we go to town
    on Saturday night,
All the streets are bright,
And stores are a-light—
When we go to town
    on Saturday night.

When we go to town,
    we know what we'll do,
We'll buy shirts and pants
And dresses all new—
When we go to town,
    that's just what we'll do.

When we go to town,
    we'll go to a show,
A Western show
With horses that go—
When we go to town,
    We'll go to a show.

Little Black Lamb

Little Black Lamb

"Here's a baby lamb for you, Rosita," said her father. "A black one."

Rosita, a little Mexican girl, came out of the sheep-wagon, where she lived with her father.

"Black!" she said. "I'll name her Blackie. Oh, her face is so pretty." She took the lamb and held it in her arms.

"Keep her warm, and give her milk," said her father, Manuel. "She make a good ewe. She be good for a marker. Mr. Walcott, he not sell her for meat in the fall."

"I take good care of Blackie," said Rosita.

"The mother sheep had twins," said Manuel. "Blackie is the little one. The ewe won't own her. She's short of milk anyhow."

"Why is she black?" asked Rosita.

"Nobody know why white ewes sometimes have black lambs," said Manuel. "Their fathers are white too. But now and then it happen. I need more black sheep, about one to a hundred head."

"It easier to count them," said Rosita.

She knew, because she often helped her father. The herder had to count two thousand sheep every day. If he had twenty black sheep in the flock, it was easier. When he missed one of the black markers, he knew that some of his flock had wandered away. Then he had to go and hunt for them.

"I must go back to my sheep," said Manuel. "The lambs are coming fast. Take care of the little black one. Come, Shep." His sheep-dog followed him back to the pasture.

Rosita was left alone at the wagon. She made a soft bed in a box. She put the lamb down. It was so weak, she was afraid it was going to die.

"Wait a minute," she said. "I feed you."

She opened a can of milk, added some water, and warmed it on the stove. She found a bottle with a nipple, and filled it. But the little black lamb would not open its mouth. It would not touch the nipple.

"You sleep first," said Rosita. She covered the lamb with a blanket and left it. She went outside and sat on the step.

Rosita was used to staying alone at the sheep-wagon. Sometimes she walked with her father and helped with the flock. But more often she stayed alone. She was eight years old, and had black eyes and hair. She was quiet and timid. Her mother had died when she was a baby. She did not have anyone to talk to but her father, Manuel.

But she always kept busy. She was a good little housekeeper. She cooked the meals and washed the dishes. She swept the floor and made up the two bunk beds. When the work was done, she sat on the step.

She sewed and mended their clothes. She watched the sky for clouds. She played with a horned toad. Toady was tame and lived in the sand just outside the door. Sometimes she hunted over the pastures for wild flowers.

Today, she sat on the step and waited. The little black lamb got warm and slept. She tried to feed it again. This time Blackie took the nipple and began to suck. Rosita was glad.

"Now she not die," said Rosita.

Manuel was glad too, when he came home that night.

"A fine ewe she'll make," he said.

At first, Rosita fed the lamb four times a day. Then, as Blackie grew stronger, only twice. Soon

the lamb was up, walking on her wobbly legs. Rosita moved her box outside and put it under the wagon. When Blackie was two weeks old, Rosita put out a little oats for her, and let her eat what she wanted.

In May, the sheep were sheared. Their heavy woollen coats were gone. They looked skinny and scared. They felt cool and crowded closely together. Rosita and Manuel had to laugh at them. Now they were ready for the heat of the summer.

Manuel stayed home more now. Wherever the sheep-wagon was, that was home. He moved the wagon to a little hill, where the sheep could bed around it and get the cool evening breeze. He sat in the shade of the wagon, on hot summer days, and watched his sheep. Shep rested, too.

Early in the morning, the sheep left the bed-ground. While it was cool, they grazed their way slowly down to the watering place. There they drank their fill. They nibbled a bite of grass here and a bite there. Then they lay down to rest. Late in the day, when the sun started to get low, they left the water-holes and came back to higher ground. They picked up their supper as they came.

One day, Manuel and Rosita watched them come back, while Blackie frisked at their feet. Suddenly they heard a loud roaring sound.

"What is it?" cried Rosita. "The sheep?" Her face turned pale with fright.

But nothing was the matter with the sheep. They were calmly eating grass.

"Do not fear, child," said Manuel. "It is only an airplane. See—it looks like a big bird flying in the sky. It will not hurt you."

He put his arm around her. Rosita had never seen an airplane before.

Then they heard loud shots.

"What is it, Papa?" asked Rosita, frightened still more.

"The men in the airplane, they shoot coyotes," said Manuel. "They shoot from the air. Poor coyote—he has no chance. His day is over. Soon there be no more coyotes to kill the sheep. That make it easy for the sheep herder."

He laughed and Rosita smiled again.

Blackie began to grow stronger. She got too big for the bottle, and began to eat grass. When she was three weeks old, she had to go back to the ranch with the other lambs.

"Mr. Walcott, he going to dock them," said Manuel.

"Oh no!" cried Rosita. "Not Blackie. He won't cut her tail off—not Blackie."

"Blackie cannot always stay a pet," said Manuel sternly. "Soon she will be big enough to run with the flock. I need her for a marker."

"Oh no!" Rosita began to cry.

When the lambs came back from the ranch, Blackie's tail was gone. Rosita cried again when she saw the blood.

"It has to be done to keep the sheep clean,"

said Manuel. "Do not be foolish, little one."

In a short time, Blackie was as frisky as ever. Rosita forgot the lamb had had a tail and lost it. Blackie grew tamer and tamer. She followed Rosita up the steps into the sheep-wagon. She curled up in the girl's lap to rest.

Rosita talked to Blackie aloud.

One day she was in the sheep-wagon talking to Blackie. She talked so loud, she did not hear her father come up the hill. He stood beside the wagon and listened. He smiled to himself.

She had fed the little black lamb and was talking to it.

"Little lambie, are you still hungry?" She asked.

Her father answered for the lamb. In a squeaky voice, he said, "Yes, Mama."

"Little lambie, are you still hungry?" Rosita asked again.

"Yes, Mama, I'm starved to death!" replied her father.

Out from the sheep-wagon dashed Rosita, wide-eyed and frightened. She fell into her father's arms. She was scared to think the lamb was talking to her. "The black lamb . . . the black lamb . . ."

Then she looked up into her father's face. She saw his big smile.

"Oh, it was *you!*" she said.

Manuel and Rosita laughed. Then Manuel's face turned sober.

"You must not set your heart on keeping your pet," he said. "Soon Blackie must run with the flock."

"Oh *no!*" cried Rosita. She dreaded the day when she would have to give her up.

The hot summer passed, and fall came. Mr. Walcott, the owner of the flock, came out to the pasture. Rosita showed him Blackie. Rosita was proud of the fine sheep she had raised.

"Is that your little black lamb, Rosita?" asked Mr. Walcott.

Rosita hung her head, too shy to answer.

"Blackie is heavier than her twin," said Manuel, "the lamb that was raised by its mother."

"You've done a good job, Rosita," said Mr. Walcott. "When we shear her, the wool will be yours."

"*Mine?*" cried Rosita. "Her wool?" She could not believe it.

"You need a warm blanket for your bed," said Mr. Walcott, "and a nice warm coat for your back. Blackie will give them to you."

"Oh . . . thank you." Rosita put her arms around Blackie's neck and hid her face in the soft wool.

Mr. Walcott turned to Manuel. "You can let Blackie run with the flock now," he said. "She'll make a good marker."

"Oh *no!*" Rosita jumped to her feet, but she could not say it out loud. It would be ungrateful, after Mr. Walcott had promised her Blackie's wool. The men walked away. Rosita sat down on the wagon step.

She did not look at the clouds now. She did not hunt for wild flowers. She did not even look at Toady, who was lying on the sand in the sun. She talked to herself. She told herself she must be unselfish. She must give Blackie up. Blackie was a full-grown sheep now. Blackie had to run with the flock. When Blackie came to put her nose in Rosita's lap, she ran into the sheep-wagon and shut the door tight. She lay down on the bunk and cried.

When Manuel took Blackie away, Rosita said nothing. Her father did not look back at her. He did not want to see the tears in her eyes. He went off without saying good-by.

For several days nothing was said. Rosita was sad and lonely without her pet. Then she asked, "How is my Blackie?"

"Your Blackie is a bad girl," said Manuel with a smile. "She think she just eat and play all day long, like when she stay with you. When the sheep go far off, I send Shep to turn them back. What that Blackie do? She chase after Shep—

she want to play with Shep, and all the other
sheep follow her."

Rosita laughed. It was funny the way Manuel
told it.

The next day, Rosita went with her father. She
looked over the flock. "Which one is Blackie?"
she asked.

"You don't know her?" asked Manuel. "There
she is. She chasing Shep just like yesterday."

Rosita saw a large black ewe bouncing up and
down, following after Shep.

"Blackie, she bad, bad girl," said Manuel.
"Today I stop her."

"What you do?" cried Rosita. "You not hurt
her?"

"I teach Blackie a lesson," said Manuel. He
called Shep back. "Go after Blackie, Shep," he
said. "Take her in the herd. *Nip her!*"

The dog knew what to do. He chased Blackie
and caught up with her. He nipped her by the
hind leg and turned her over in a somersault.
Blackie fell so hard, it knocked the wind out of
her.

"Oh!" cried Rosita. "Oh!"

"That good for silly old Blackie," said Manuel. "That teach her something."

Blackie got to her feet and looked around. She saw Rosita, and she came straight to her. Rosita knew the ewe wanted to rest her head in her lap. She wanted sympathy.

But before Blackie could reach the girl, Manuel stepped out and gave the ewe a sharp kick.

"*Papa!*" cried Rosita, angry now. "Why you do that?" She rushed at her father with her fists clenched.

"Blackie got to learn," said Manuel. "A lamb

has got to learn like a child. She got to learn to mind when she young. We learn the hard way when we get older."

Rosita said no more. She knew Blackie was not the only one who had to learn. She had to learn a lesson too.

Winter came and every day Rosita went out to find wood. She kept the fire going in the little stove. The sheep-wagon was as cozy and warm as any home. Smoke poured out of the stove-pipe on one side.

Rosita no longer sat on the wagon step. She sat on a chair inside, by the window. She waited for her father to come. The days were very long because there was nothing to do.

One day Manuel took his gun out.

"I lost some sheep," he said. "I think it a coyote."

"Where is the bird flying in the air?" asked Rosita.

"The airplane?" said Manuel. "Not here when we need it. Maybe it not a coyote—maybe a pack of dogs from town. I soon find out."

"I go with you," said Rosita. "I take *tamales* for lunch."

She bundled up and walked along with her father. They stayed near the flock all day and watched the sheep. But nothing happened. They sat down at midday and ate their *tamales*. At dusk they started home.

Suddenly they heard sheep-bells jingling. Manuel ran back, with Shep beside him.

A few sheep had gone over the hill, away from the flock. A gray coyote sneaked up out of a draw to get them. The sheep began to run, the

coyote after them. The coyote was just grabbing
the leg of a black sheep, when Manuel came over
the hill. Manuel fired a shot. The coyote dodged
and got away.

"It was that bad girl Blackie," Manuel said.
"She won't run fast enough."

"The coyote got her?" asked Rosita, wide-
eyed.

"No," said Manuel. "A close shave. My shot
scared the coyote off."

That night, Manuel moved the flock to higher
land, nearer the sheep-wagon. Then he and Rosita went to bed. In the middle of the night, a jingling of sheep-bells brought the herder to his
feet, wide awake. Out he went, with Shep beside
him. Rosita slept so soundly, she heard nothing.

When she awoke, Manuel brought good news.
The coyote was dead. The sheep—and Blackie—
were safe.

May came again, and sheep-shearing time.
Manuel drove the flock to the shearing-sheds at
the ranch. Rosita went with him to watch.

The shearers worked fast with their clippers.

They clipped the wool off the sheep, put it in great bags and tramped it down. Rosita watched the sheep in the pen outside, she waited and waited.

Then Blackie came in at the gate. Her eyes were rolling with fright. Rosita wanted to call out to her above the loud bleating of the hundreds of sheep and the loud clatter of the motors. She wanted to say, "It's all right, Blackie. They won't hurt you. They only want to clip your wool off. It will make you cool for summer."

But Blackie was not a pet any more. She was

one of several thousand sheep.

Rosita looked again. *Was* it her Blackie?

The shearer had tied a rope around her legs, and thrown her down. He was stripping the wool off her, in swift movements of his clippers.

Other black sheep came through the gate too. Each one was as wild-eyed and frightened as the first Blackie. Each one was as frightened as the hundreds of white sheep. *Which one was Blackie?* Rosita did not know.

She looked at the sheep in the pen. They were shorn and shivering. They crowded close to keep warm. They did not know each other. And Rosita did not know a single one.

At last she was able to give Blackie up. There would be other little motherless lambs to love and care for.

At the end of the day, Rosita thanked Mr. Walcott for the big sack of wool he gave her. When winter came, she would have a warm blanket to pull up to her chin, and a warm coat for her back.

She thought of Blackie happily now. The little black lamb had started on milk. She ate green

grass in the spring and early summer. She ate
dark brown grass in the fall and winter. Sometimes she ate grain. No matter what Blackie ate,
it went into her body, and through some wonderful change, grew into soft wool—wool for Rosita's blanket and coat. The coat that Blackie
wore last winter to keep warm, Rosita would
wear next winter herself.

Rosita smiled happily. She took her father's
hand, and they walked slowly home—home to
the sheep-wagon on the hill.

Desert Sand

The hot sun shines
On the desert sand;
The horned toad turns
And moves on my hand.

Catclaw and cactus
With blooms alight,
Cover the pasture
With flowers bright.

Down to the water-hole,
There go the sheep;
Down in the cool shade
To rest and sleep.

Follow the leader—
Little lamb so black—
Nibbling the grass
On the well-worn track.

Pine Tree House

Pine Tree House

Cecil and His Goat

A little unpainted house sat at the edge of the piny woods. The ground was bare and hard around it. At the sides in the high grass, little pine trees grew. Beyond, a circle of tall, tall pine trees threw dark shadows over the ground.

"Hi, Daddy! Hi, Daddy!"

Cecil came running out of the door. He was a small boy with a high, squeaky voice. His little brother Curry, still smaller, came out too. There was Daddy in his truck. Daddy backed it up and climbed out.

"What you got, Daddy?" asked Cecil.

Daddy untied a rope. Down jumped a little gray goat with horns. The boys stared.

"A goat!" said Cecil. "Where did you get it, Daddy?"

"Made a trade with a man down the road," said Daddy.

The door of the house opened again and Mama came out. She held the baby on her arm.

"What you got now, Walter?" she asked.

"Just a little ole billy goat, Beulah," said Daddy. "Now don't you stir up a fuss."

"A goat!" said Mama. "Who wants a goat?"

"I do," said Cecil.

"So do I," said Curry.

Daddy tied the goat's rope to the limb of a tree. The goat jumped up and down and began to eat the leaves. Even Mama had to laugh.

Cecil was not afraid. He went over and patted the goat.

"He's tame, Mama," said Cecil. "He likes to be petted."

"Goats are bad," said Mama. "I don't want a goat around here."

"He can stay in the shed," said Daddy.

"Keep him over at the sawmill then." Mama turned her back and went inside.

Daddy and the boys led the goat away.

There was Cousin Jesse's sawmill down the road a piece. An old shed covered the big saws. A sawdust pile as high as a house rose up at one side.

Daddy opened a small door and put the goat in the shed. The goat scratched himself and rubbed against the wall. He sniffed and looked around.

"Lie down, goat!" said Cecil.

But the goat did not lie down.

"Does he sleep standing up?" asked Curry.

Daddy laughed.

Daddy knew what little boys liked. The next morning he said, "Cecil, want to play with your goat? Go get your wagon."

Cecil brought the wagon and they went over to the sawmill. Daddy made shafts for the front of the wagon. He made a harness for the goat. He used old sacks to make collar and traces. He hitched the goat up to the wagon.

"Now, go to it," said Daddy.

Cecil got in the wagon and said *giddy-ap*.

The goat did not move.

"He'll learn to pull you," said Daddy.

Daddy drove away in his truck. He hauled logs for Cousin Jesse. He had to go to the piny woods and get a big load.

Cecil said *giddy-ap* again, but the goat did not go.

"Get me a stick," said Cecil.

Curry broke a stick off a tree. Cecil whipped the goat to make it go. The goat took hold of the stick and ate it up. The boys laughed.

"I want a ride too," said Curry.

"Get on, then," said Cecil.

Curry climbed on the wagon behind Cecil. Just then the goat started. It ran very fast and the boys had to hold on tight. It came to the sawdust pile and ran halfway up the side. The pile was so steep, the boys fell out of the wagon and went tumbling down.

They jumped up again, laughing. Sawdust was in their hair and eyes and ears. Sawdust was in their sleeves and pockets and in the rolls of their overalls. They had to shake and shake to get the sawdust off.

"What you got there?" somebody asked.

Cecil looked up and saw Susie Bob. With her were her little sisters, Sylvia and Maxine. They were Cousin Jesse's girls, but Cecil did not like them much. Susie Bob was very bossy.

"What you got there?" she asked again.

"A goat," said Cecil.

"Where'd you get it?" asked Susie Bob.

"I won't tell you," said Cecil.

He ran up the sawdust pile and dragged goat and wagon down.

"Give us a ride," begged Susie Bob.

"No," said Cecil. "My goat's not trained yet. Where's Harvey?"

Harvey was her brother and Cecil liked Harvey.

"He went down to Archie's store," said Susie Bob. "He had to get some stuff for Mama."

Susie Bob was being very nice now, because she wanted a ride.

"Who made the harness?" asked Susie Bob.

"My daddy did," said Cecil.

"Who taught the goat to pull the wagon?"

"I did," said Cecil, bragging.

"Give me a ride," begged Susie Bob.

"No," said Cecil. "Harvey can ride, but not you."

Cecil felt very proud of his goat. Cousin Jesse's children had never had a goat. The goat made Cecil feel very important. He took Curry on the back of the wagon and they rode round and round. Each time Cecil said *giddy-ap* the goat went. Each time he said *whoa,* it stopped. Sometimes it nibbled leaves or grass. But when Cecil said *giddy-ap,* it went on again.

Susie Bob and her sisters got tired of watching. They went over to the sawdust pile. All the children in the neighborhood liked to play there. It was more fun than playing in sand. The girls climbed to the top and slid down on boards. They dug holes in the sawdust and hid in them. They played hide-and-seek.

Cousin Jesse's sawmill was a busy place. Trucks loaded with logs came in and were unloaded. Men put the logs on a moving belt, which took them up to the big rotary saw under the shed roof. The saw sliced the bark off, first on one side, then, as the log turned over, on the three other sides. After that, the saw sawed the logs into planks. The planks were stood up on their ends and left to cure or dry in the sun.

Whenever it sawed, the saw made a loud screeching sound. And sawdust poured out of a big long pipe on top of the sawdust pile.

The girls put their hands over their ears when they heard the noise of the saw. Once they ran out under the shower of fresh sawdust just for fun. But a man came and told them to go away. He sent them back by the ditch, where the old sawdust was. They waited for Cecil and his goat to come up. They had their hands full of sawdust to throw on him.

"Look! The goat's running fast!" cried Sylvia.

"Here they come," said Maxine.

"The goat's running *away!*" said Susie Bob.

Goat and wagon and boys came running. But the goat got there first, leaving the boys far behind. They had been dumped off the wagon by the side of the road. Then the harness had broken and the wagon had been left behind. The goat chased the girls, who dropped their sawdust and ran. The goat ran up to the very top of the sawdust pile. It stood there, looking down at the boys.

Cecil and Curry got up, rubbing their bumped knees.

Cecil saw the goat and laughed.

"Goat's up on top of the world!" he said.

Cecil in the Woods

One morning Mama opened the lean-to door and came out with her broom. The door wobbled and fell off its hinges.

"This old house is falling to pieces," said Mama. "I'll be glad when we get a new one."

"A new house?" said Cecil, in surprise.

To Cecil, there was nothing wrong with the old one. There were two rooms and a porch, with a lean-to for cooking, built of scrap lumber. The cracks in the floor were so big, Cecil could put a stick down and scratch the back of a razorback hog sleeping there. The hogs liked the cool shade under the house. Every day when Mama mopped the floor, the water ran down through the cracks like rain. The house was old, but Cecil liked it. It was his home.

"Are we gonna get a new house?" asked Cecil.

"Yes, Cousin Jesse's cutting our timber now,"

said Mama. "All those pine logs that Daddy is hauling to the sawmill will be sawed into lumber and used for our new house."

"A pine tree house!" cried Cecil.

Cecil untied his goat, jumped on its back and went riding round and round.

"A pine tree house!" cried Cecil. "We're gonna get us a pine tree house!"

Daddy came up with an iron stake.

"Get off that goat, Cecil," he said, "and come here. You can't play with the goat all the time. You'll run him to death."

Daddy tied the goat's rope to the stake. He staked the goat out in the high grass.

"Let him eat today," said Daddy. "Goats like grass to eat. Move the stake after he eats the grass and bushes off clean. Break off some leaves from the tree for him to eat."

Then Daddy went away in the truck. Cecil hated to stop riding. The goat was fun, but he knew it must eat. He gave it some leaves and walked off.

He went over to the sawdust pile. All the children were there. Some were walking on the logs, their arms held out to balance. Harvey and another boy called J. W. were rolling old auto tires down the sawdust pile. The girls were playing house. They had an old iron stove. They cooked acorns for beans, and leaves for turnip greens. They used gravel from the road for money.

The children saw Cecil and came running. He knew what they wanted.

"Where's your goat?" they asked. "Can we have a ride?"

Cecil shook his head. He felt very important. He was the only one who had a goat.

"Goat's hungry," he said. "He's got to eat. Can't ride today."

Disappointed, the children went back to their play.

Cecil called to J. W. and said, "Let's go to our woods."

J. W. said, "O.K. Let's go."

J. W. was Cecil's best friend. He had red hair and freckles and a big wide smile. He always did what Cecil wanted.

Cecil and J. W. started off to the piny woods where the men were logging. Curry came too, because he always went where Cecil went. They walked a long way under the tall, tall pines till they came to Daddy's woods. They chased razor-back hogs and tried to catch a squirrel. They scared up a few rabbits and ran after them. The pine needles felt soft on the soles of their bare feet. The scent of the pines was sweet on the breeze.

Soon they came to an open clearing. Many stumps showed where tall trees had been cut. Now the men were working over at one side. They were cutting logs to take to the sawmill.

Fallen trees lay on the ground beside their stumps.

Uncle Tom, Daddy's brother, and another man had a gasoline saw and were sawing down a large tree. The saw made a loud whining noise. Nearby a bulldozer was pushing logs to a truck where they were being loaded. The boys saw Daddy start off for the sawmill with a truckload of logs. They waved to him as he passed by.

"Let's climb up in our tree-house," said Cecil.

"O.K.," said J. W.

The summer before, the boys had found a favorite pine tree that was higher than the rest. It made a good look-out. They had nailed boards on the trunk so they could climb all the way up. They had made a seat at the top.

Now they climbed up and perched there like birds. They pretended to spot forest fires in the distance. They watched the men at work. They watched the trucks and bulldozers come and go. They heard the roar of the trucks and the whine of the saws.

Suddenly Curry shouted, "Look who's coming!"

A man in a jeep came up the road. He came
into the woods with a can of paint and a brush.
He walked from tree to tree. He painted yellow
X's on some of them.

"He's marking the trees to be cut," said J. W.,
"the big ones that are big enough for sawlogs.
They only cut the biggest ones. The little ones
have to grow some more."

"Just so he doesn't mark our tree-house tree,"
said Cecil.

"He won't," said J. W. "He'll see our steps on
it. He'll know we want to keep it."

But Cecil was not so sure. The man kept coming closer and closer. Soon he was right below them. He was putting his brush in the can of paint.

"Hey, you!" called J. W. "Don't mark this tree-house tree. This is our look-out. We spot forest fires from here."

The man looked up and laughed. He sized up the tree, painted a big yellow X on it, and started to go away.

"Better get down, boys, before the saw comes," he said.

"He can't do this to us!" cried Cecil.

The three boys climbed down quickly, but they were too late. The man was already in his jeep and had gone down the road.

The boys looked up at the yellow X in dismay.

"Jeepers!" said Cecil.

"Can't we rub it off?" asked J. W.

He pulled some leaves and tried to rub the yellow paint off. But it had sunk in the bark too deeply.

"*I* know!" cried Cecil. "I'll tell my daddy. I'll tell Cousin Jesse. *They* won't let him saw our tree-house tree down."

"Let's go quick!" said Curry. "Let's take the short-cut."

The three boys started on a run to go home. The short-cut lay across a branch. They rolled up their overalls and waded to the other side. The water was warm, they forgot their hurry and waded a while. On the other side was a stand of young seedling pines.

"Let's play Tarzan in the jungle!" said J. W.

He took off his wrist watch and hung it on a limb for safekeeping. The boys swung back and forth on the saplings, having fun. The afternoon was passing, and the setting sun made long shadows in the woods. Then Cecil remembered the yellow X on their tree.

"Come on!" he cried. "I gotta tell Cousin Jesse."

They came to a barbed wire fence and Cecil tried to climb over it. In his hurry, his overalls caught and he came down on the wire and cut his leg. It began to bleed.

Curry and J. W. looked at it and were scared.

"It's not cut so bad," said J. W.

"Yes, it is," said Curry. "It's cut deep. Look

at all the blood."

After that, they could not hurry much. Cecil's leg hurt and he had to limp. He leaned on J. W. and held Curry's arm. Then J. W. remembered he had left his wrist watch behind, so he went back to get it. Curry helped Cecil hobble all the way home.

Before they got there, they heard Daddy calling.

They answered, "Yoo-hoo! We're coming!"

They came up as quickly as they could. It was nearly dark now. Daddy was hopping mad. He was shouting in a loud voice.

"Why did you go off and leave that goat? Why didn't you pen him up in the shed if you were going off? Look what he's done!"

It was dark but not too dark to see. The lean-to had fallen down. It was only a pile of old lumber now—with the kitchen stove in the middle. Mama was trying to pull chairs and table out of the wreckage. The baby was in the front room crying.

"That goat climbed up on the table!" said Mama. "It butted the roof off and knocked the house down. I thought it was an earthquake and I like to died. He broke all my dishes and knocked down all my pots. We've got to sell him."

There was nothing to eat for supper. Cecil undressed and was crawling into bed when Mama saw blood on his leg.

"How did you hurt it?" she asked.

"Barb wire," said Cecil.

Mama washed the cut and tied a rag around. "We've got to sell him!"

Mama's words kept going over and over in Cecil's mind and he could not sleep.

Cecil's New House

"We've got to sell that goat!" Mama said.

All the next day Cecil's leg was stiff and he could not walk. Mama talked about selling the goat, but Daddy said nothing. He moved the stove into the front room and put the stove-pipe out the window. Mama found her pans so she could cook again. Aunt Ellie, Uncle Tom's wife, sent over some dishes so they could eat.

Curry had to take care of the goat. He staked it out to eat grass. Then he took it over to the saw-mill and let the children ride.

Cecil sat in a chair on the front porch and watched. He saw Harvey and J. W. ride the goat up and down the sawdust pile. They made a stack of old boxes and had the goat climb up and jump off. Then the girls drove the goat in his wagon. Cecil felt very sorry for himself. He wanted to be there too.

When Daddy came home at noon, Cecil asked him about the tree-house tree.

"You won't let them cut it, will you, Daddy?"

"Son," said Daddy, "that woods is mine. I've watched those pine trees grow since I was a kid like you. I've put fires out and tended them all these years. Now they are ready for the market. All the big trees must be cut to make room for the little ones. I want them to grow big and tall too."

"But can't you leave just one?" asked Cecil. "Our tree-house tree?"

"Son," said Daddy. "Your tree's already cut."

Cecil felt so sad that Daddy tried to cheer him up.

"I'll tell you what," said Daddy. "After it's well seasoned, we'll use it for the main roof timber in our new house—to hold the roof up. How's that?"

Cecil looked up and smiled.

Daddy was in good humor now. So Cecil said, "You won't sell the goat, will you, Daddy?"

"Hum . . . we'll see," said Daddy, walking away. "It depends on how he behaves."

Cecil sat in his chair all day long. His leg kept on hurting and he felt very lonely. He listened to the sharp toots of the sawmill's whistle, and he counted the logging trucks as they went by.

In the evening, when Curry tried to put the goat in the shed, the goat dragged him round and round the yard at the end of the long rope. Mama had to come and put the goat up.

Just before dark Cecil heard a loud crash. "Look!" he cried. "A wreck! It's Daddy's truck!"

Mama and Curry came running. Mama brought the baby and they sat on the porch to watch.

Daddy's truck, loaded with lumber for the new house, had had a blow-out. It had run into the ditch on the other side of the black-top road.

Then the excitement began. A police car came and set a row of flares. Another truck came and stopped, then the man drove off to get a new tire.

Another man came from the sawmill to help. He and Daddy unloaded the lumber and stacked it under a tree. They fastened a chain to the truck's axle and used another truck to pull it out of the ditch. When the new tire came, the men changed it. They loaded the lumber back on the truck, ready to be hauled to the new house the next day. Then Daddy came home.

After Cecil's leg got well, Daddy started building the new house in the clearing in the piny woods. He hauled cement blocks for the foundation, and then the frame went up, with Cousin

Jesse and Uncle Tom helping. Time passed. Cecil's tree was gone now. It was a big square beam to hold the roof up.

After that, Cecil went to the new house every day to watch the work. He took the goat along and staked it in the grass and bushes nearby. Daddy gave Cecil hammer and nails and told him what to do to help. After the house was framed in with pine wood, Daddy did all the finishing alone.

At home, Mama was getting ready to move. She bought feed sacks in pretty colors and made new curtains. She washed all her bedding and dried it in the sun. She made two new quilts. Over at the new house, she put pretty wallpaper on the walls. She painted the woodwork too.

It was not long before they were ready to move in. Daddy took the furniture over on the truck, and Mama put her new dishes and her old pots in the new kitchen. Then she had to buy groceries.

"Come, Cecil," she called. "Come and help me."

Archie's store was down at the end of the road beyond the sawmill. Cecil went along with

Mama to carry the sacks. They walked slowly at the edge of the black-top, so the trucks would not hit them.

They had not gone far when they heard a sharp pitter-patter behind them. Mama turned and said, "Oh, that goat! He's coming too!"

"Good!" said Cecil, with a laugh. "I'll just take a ride!"

He jumped on the goat's back, patted it on the head, and made it walk quietly behind Mama.

"Don't let him butt me!" cried Mama, walking faster and faster.

The goat kept right at her heels, but it did not butt her at all. At the store, it followed her in and stood right in front of her. It licked her hand, then jumped up on the counter.

"The goat likes you, Mama," said Cecil.

"Oh no!" said Mama. "He's just hungry. He wants me to feed him."

She picked an apple out of a box and held it out to the goat. The goat ate it and looked for more.

Archie and his customers crowded round to see. Cousin Jesse's wife and children were there, and J. W. and his mother and sister. Archie handed out a stick of candy and Mama gave it to the goat. He handed out an orange and bubble gum and cookies and candy marbles. The goat ate them all. Archie brought out a can of toma-

toes. The goat sniffed it and knocked it to the floor.

"What? You don't like tin cans?" said Archie, laughing.

All the people laughed. Cecil laughed most of all.

Mama was not mad at the goat any more. She laughed and told how the goat had knocked over the lean-to, so Daddy had to build their new house.

"You like the goat now, don't you, Mama?" said Cecil. "You won't sell it, will you?"

"Well, I might if somebody offers me a good price," said Mama.

A man in the store handed out a dollar. "I'll buy him," he said.

"Oh . . ." said Mama. "I was only fooling. I . . . I don't think I want to sell the goat . . ."

"I'll give you a dollar," said the man.

"The goat's not worth twenty-five cents," said Mama. "I hated him at first, but he's so tame now and does what we tell him to. He's a nice pet and so much fun for the boys . . ."

Mama would not sell the goat, so Cecil was

happy. When Archie gave Mama her groceries, he put in an extra sack of apples. Cecil rode the goat all the way home and Mama had to carry the groceries, after all.

At the old house Daddy picked them up in his truck and drove them to the new one. The furniture was all in place now. The new curtains were up and the new quilts were on the beds. Mama lighted a lamp and set it on the table. Supper would soon be ready.

Cecil put the goat in its new shed and locked the door. He came back to the pine tree house and was happy.

It looked just like home.

Great Big Tree

Tree, tree, oh great big tree,
Tell me, what do you give to me?

I keep off the sun
  On a hot summer day,
In the cool of my shade
  You may rest and play.

I give you good heat
  On a cold winter night,
When logs on your hearth
  Are burning bright.

My wood for your house,
  Your table, your door,
Your hoe handle strong,
  The boards of your floor.

I give you your house
  Of timber tall,
I keep storms away
  From roof and wall.